D1596067

EOS

OR

THE WIDER ASPECTS OF COSMOGONY

PLATE I

[*Mt. Wilson Observatory*

The spiral nebula (M. 81) in Ursa Major.

A TYPICAL SPIRAL NEBULA.

[*front*

EOS

OR

THE WIDER ASPECTS OF COSMOGONY

By

JAMES HOPWOOD JEANS

Select Bibliographies Reprint Series

BOOKS FOR LIBRARIES PRESS
FREEPORT, NEW YORK

First Published 1928
Reprinted 1969

STANDARD BOOK NUMBER:
8369-5091-7

LIBRARY OF CONGRESS CATALOG CARD NUMBER:
73-99662

PRINTED IN THE UNITED STATES OF AMERICA

LIST OF ILLUSTRATIONS

LIST OF ILLUSTRATIONS

FOREWORD

This little book contains the Trueman Wood Lecture delivered before the Royal Society of Arts on 7th March, 1928, expanded to more than double its original length by the addition of what I would have liked to say, but had not time to, at the lecture, and by the inclusion of a small part of an earlier lecture "Recent Developments of Cosmical Physics" delivered before the University of London on 9th November, 1926. My thanks are offered to the Royal Society of Arts, and also to the Editor of "Nature" in whose columns the reports of these lectures first appeared, for permission to use them in preparing the present book.

While the "To-day and To-morrow" series has been the medium of publication of many brilliant flights of imagination, the present book is limited to scientific facts and such inferences as I think may properly be drawn from them. Happily astronomy is a science in which exact truth is ever stranger than fiction, in which the imagination ever labours panting and breathless behind the reality, and about which one could hardly be prosaic if one tried.

J. H. JEANS.

DORKING,
12th May, 1928.

EOS

Interest in scientific cosmogony is a recent, and still a very tender growth. Anthropologists and geologists tell us that man has existed on earth for something like 300,000 years; we must go this far back to meet our ape-like ancestry. Between them and us some 10,000 generations of men have walked the earth, most of whom have probably given some thought, in varying degrees, to the significance of their existence and the plan of the universe.

Of these 10,000 generations of men, the first 9990 unhesitatingly regarded the earth as the centre, and terrestrial life as the central fact, of the universe. As was suited to its majesty and dignity as the abode of man, the earth stood still while the celestial sphere spun round it, covering in the earth much as a telescope-dome covers in the telescope; and this dome was spangled with stars, which had been thoughtfully added so as not to leave the central earth unillumined at night. Ten generations at most have been able to view the problem of their existence in anything like its proper astronomical perspective.

THE POSITION OF MAN IN THE UNIVERSE

The total age of the earth far exceeds the 300,000 years or so of man's existence. The evidence of geology, and of radio-activity in rocks in particular, shows that it must be something like 2000 million years, which is several thousand times the age of the human race. Old Mother Earth must regard man as a very recent apparition indeed; he has just appeared to burrow into her, burn her forests, put her waterfalls into pipes, and generally mar the beauty of her features. If he has done so much in the first few moments of his existence, she may well wonder what is in store for her in the long future ages in which he is destined to labour on her surface. For in all probability the life in front of the human race must enormously exceed the short life behind it. A million million years hence, so far as we can foresee, the sun will probably still be much as now, and the earth will be revolving round it much as now. The year will be a little longer, and the climate quite a lot colder, while the rich accumulated stores of coal, oil, and forest will have long been burnt up; but there is no reason why our descendants should not still people the earth. Perhaps it may be unable to support so large a population as now, and perhaps fewer will desire to live on it. On the other hand, mankind, being theee million times as old as now, may—if the conjecture does not distress our pessimists too much—be three million times as wise.

Looked at on the astronomical time-scale, humanity is at the very beginning of its existence—a new-born babe, with all the unexplored potentialities of babyhood; and until the last few moments its interest has been centred, absolutely and exclusively, on its cradle and feeding-bottle. It has just become conscious of the vast world existing outside itself and its cradle; it is learning to focus its eyes on distant objects, and its awakening brain is beginning to wonder, in a vague, dreamy way, what they are and what purpose they serve. Its interest in this external world is not much developed yet, so that the main part of its faculties is still engrossed with the cradle and feeding-bottle, but a little corner of its brain is beginning to wonder.

Taking a very gloomy view of the future of the human race, let us suppose that it can only expect to survive for two thousand million years longer, a period about equal to the past age of the earth. Then, regarded as a being destined to live for three-score years and ten, humanity, although it has been born in a house seventy years old, is itself only three days old. But only in the last few minutes has it become conscious that the whole world does not centre round its cradle and its trappings, and only in the last few ticks of the clock has any adequate conception of the size of the external world dawned upon it. For our clock does not tick seconds, but years; its minutes are the lives of men. A minute and a half ago the distance of a star was first measured and provided a measuring-rod for the universe. Less than a quarter of a minute has elapsed since Professor Hertzsprung of Leiden and Dr. Shapley, now Director of Harvard Observatory, showed how the peculiar stars known as Cepheid variables provide a longer measuring-rod, and taught us to think in distances so great that light takes hundreds of thousands of years to traverse them. With the very last tick of the clock, Dr. Hubble, of Mount Wilson Observatory, using the same measuring-rod, has found that the most remote objects visible in the biggest telescope on earth are so distant that light, travelling 186,000 miles a second, takes about 140 million years to come from them to us.

Not only is our vision of the universe continually expanding, but also it is expanding at an ever-increasing rate. Is this expansion destined to go on for ever? So far as we can at present see, no; for a general guiding principle, that of generalised relativity, fixes a limit, which we are fast approaching. According to this theory, space cannot extend for ever; it has no limit, but is nevertheless finite like the surface of the earth. Without exploring and surveying the whole of the earth's surface, we can make a fair estimate of its total area by measuring its radius, which we can do by measuring its curvature at any one point. In the same way the total volume of space is fixed by a quantity, the curvature of space, which can be determined by measuring the density of distribution of matter in space. Space which contained no matter would go on for ever, but the parts of space we can survey with our telescopes contain enough matter to show that we already see an appreciable fraction of the whole of space. It is as though our baby, watching ships coming from over the horizon, concluded that the earth's surface was curved, and formed a general rough conception of its size by imagining the observed curvature continuing until the earth's surface rounded back on itself.

Exact figures are impossible, but Dr. Hubble has calculated that space is not likely to extend to more than about a thousand times as far as the farthest nebula visible in the biggest telescope. Nothing prevents our going on and on in space beyond this distance, but, if we do, we merely come back to ourselves. The possessor of a sufficiently sensitive wireless apparatus may emit signals and pick them up a seventh of a second later after they have travelled round the world. In the same way a not inconceivable increase in the size of our telescopes would take us round the whole of space, and we should see the stars surrounding our sun by light which had travelled round the universe, not of course as they now are, but as they were 100,000 million years ago.

Such considerations make it improbable that the expansion of the universe can continue at its present rate for much longer. Having grasped that the world is round, the infant speedily forms a fair idea of its size. Our particular infant, mankind, has made the great discovery of the existence of the outer world, has formed some conception of its size, and adjusted his ideas, not by a process of slow revelation, but by a brain-flash of the last few seconds. In his mature years and his staid old age he is no doubt destined to make many sensational discoveries, but he can never again live through the immortal moment at which he first grasped the immensity of the outer world. We only live through a few ticks of his clock, and fate might have ordained that they should be anywhere in the three days that the child has already lived, or in the seventy long, and possibly tedious, years yet to come. The wonderful thing is that she has selected for us what is, perhaps, in some ways the most sensational moment of all in the life of our race.

The child sets its newly awakened mind to work to adjust and co-ordinate a new array of facts. If the world was not made to surround its cradle, what purpose can it serve? If the lights of the great ships in the harbour were not designed to light its nursery at night, what can they possibly be for? And, most interesting problem of all, if the world is such a big affair, can there be other cradles and other babies?

These remarks will have served their purpose if they suggest that the cosmogony of 1928 should not be judged as a finished science or the solution of a problem; it is rather the first confused gropings of the infant mind trying to understand the world outside its cradle. And if the impression produced by its first inexperienced glance at the outer world had to be described in a single word, it would probably select the word "immensity".

The Immensity of Space

The immensity of space is measured by the figures already mentioned. Light and wireless signals travel at the same rate because, of course, they are essentially the same thing; and this thing takes a seventh of a second to travel round the world, and probably something like 100,000 million years to travel round the universe. The ratio of these times (2×10^{19}) [1] measures the dimensions of

[1] Here, as elsewhere, 2×10^{19} is an abbreviation for 2 followed by 19 zeros, or 20,000,000,000,000,000,000. A million is 10^6, a million million is 10^{12}, and so on. The largest number which occurs in the present book is $10^{420,000,000,000}$. Failing our convenient mathematical shorthand, this number would be expressed by a 1 followed by six million volumes similar to the present, all full of 0's.

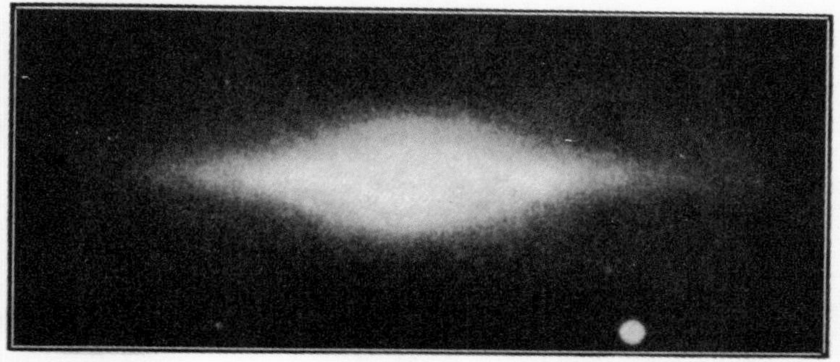

[*Mt. Wilson Observatory*

Fig. 1. Regular shaped nebula (N.G.C.3115).

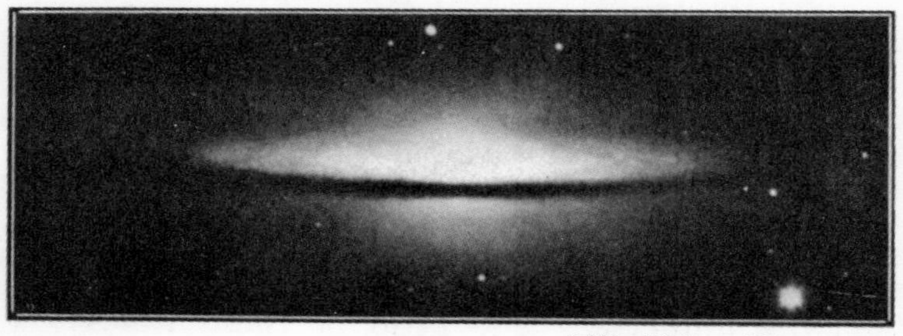

[*Mt. Wilson Observatory*

Fig. 2. Regular shaped nebula (N.G.C.4594) with ring of dark matter surrounding equator.

TWO EARLY STAGES OF NEBULAR DEVELOPMENT.

[*face p. 18*

the universe in terms of the familiar dimensions of the world; incidentally, it also measures the expansion of our spatial ideas since Copernicus. The disparity of size is too great to be easily visualised. Suppose the size of our earth represented by a single atom, whose diameter is about a hundred-millionth part of an inch. Then the range of vision of the biggest telescope is about represented by the whole earth, and the size of the whole universe, according to the theory of relativity, is represented by a stack of a thousand million earths.

Scarcely less bewildering than the immense extent of space is the immense amount and variety of matter it contains. The sun, which is a million times as big as the earth and 300,000 times as massive, proves to be something less than a grain of sand on the seashore. It forms one of a family whose number must certainly be counted in thousands of millions; Dr. Seares has estimated it at thirty thousand millions. This is not the only family of stars in space. Each of the great spiral and other extragalactic nebulæ, such as are shown in the Frontispiece and in Plates II and III is either a family of stars, or consists of stars in the making, or of matter which is in all probability destined ultimately to form stars.

We can estimate the masses of these great nebulæ by gravitational means, and each is found to contain enough matter to make a thousand million suns. This of itself will give some conception of the vast size of these nebulæ, but to tell the whole story, it must be added that their colossal masses are so tenuous that each millionth part of an ounce is, on the average, as big as the Matterhorn. Think of a body which is bigger than the Matterhorn by as much as a thousand million suns is heavier than a millionth part of an ounce, and we have the size of any one of these great nebulæ. Any one of the photographs reproduced in this book would have to

[Mt. Wilson Observatory

Fig. 3. Spiral nebula (N.G.C.891) seen edge-on.

A LATER STAGE OF NEBULAR DEVELOPMENT.

[*face p. 20*

be enlarged so as to cover at least the whole of Asia before a body of the size of the earth became visible in it at all, even under the most powerful of microscopes.

Dr. Hubble estimates that about two million such nebulæ are visible in the great 100-inch telescope at Mount Wilson, and that the whole universe is about a thousand million times as big as the part of space which is visible in this telescope. Let us now multiply 1000 million by 2 million, and the product by 1000 million. The answer (2×10^{24}) gives some indication of the probable number of stars in the universe; the same number of grains of sand spread over England would make a layer hundreds of yards in depth. Let us reflect that our earth is one millionth part of one such grain of sand, and our mundane affairs, our troubles and our achievements, begin to appear in their correct proportion to the universe as a whole.

The Variety of the Stars

While the stars may be compared to grains of sand in number, they differ too much *inter se* for the comparison to be carried further. They used to be regarded as mere points of light which differed from one another in glory but were too remote for any investigation as to their nature and condition to be practicable. Astronomy can now take their temperatures, by methods similar to those used with factory furnaces, can measure their sizes with a specially-designed stellar interferometer, and can calculate their weights from the gravitational pull they exert on companion stars, just as we calculate the weight of the earth from the pull it exerts on the moon to keep it in its orbit. And the measurements disclose an immense variety of big and little stars, of bright and faint stars, and of hot, hotter and still hotter stars.

The faintest star known, Wolf 359,

emits only a fifty-thousandth part of the light of the sun. If this star were suddenly substituted for the sun, the seas would immediately freeze into solid ice, and the atmosphere condense into liquid air; people at the Equator would receive rather less light and heat from their new sun than one receives from a coal fire a mile away, and we should meet an icy death. At the other extreme, the most luminous of known stars, S Doradus, emits 300,000 times as much light and heat as the sun. If this star were to replace our sun, our temperatures would run up to about 7,000 degrees Centigrade, which is about twice the temperature of the hottest part of the electric arc, and the solid earth, with its cloud capped towers and gorgeous palaces and ourselves, would immediately dissolve into vapour.

There is almost as much variety in the sizes of the stars. The smallest known star, Van Maanen's star, is about the size of the earth; a million such stars could be packed inside the sun and leave room to spare. The largest known star, Betelgeux, is so large that 25 million suns could be packed inside it. If we represent the sun by a golf-ball, Van Maanen's star becomes something smaller than the dot of an 'i' on this page, while Betelgeux must be represented by a good-sized house. If Van Maanen's star were to replace our sun, it would appear smaller than Jupiter or Saturn; if Betelgeux were to replace our sun, we should find ourselves inside it, its radius being greater than that of the earth's orbit.

As compared with their enormous ranges of brightness and size, ranges greater than those between a searchlight and a glow-worm, or between balloons and bird-shot, the stars shew a restful uniformity in their weights. No star exists whose weight is known or suspected to be less than about a tenth of that of the sun, while few exist which have as much as ten times the sun's weight—probably about one in a hundred thousand, the other 99,999 all having weights between a tenth and ten times the weight of the sun.

It follows that the different sizes of the stars do not result to any great extent from the different amounts of matter the stars contain; they result rather from the varying closeness or looseness with which the matter is packed. An average ton of matter in the sun occupies about as much space as an ordinary ton of coal in a coal-cellar, but the same amount of matter in Betelgeux takes up as much room as the Albert Hall, while the average ton of matter in Van Maanen's star takes up only as much room as a pea in a pea-pod; a hundred tons of it could be packed into a pocket book with ease. Judged by the standards of solidity which prevail on Van Maanen's star, everything on earth is of the very filmiest of gossamer.

The Structure of the Stars

Their enormous differences of brightness, size and density notwithstanding, the stars are believed to be essentially similar structures.

A normal atom consists of a central nucleus around which a number of electrons revolve in orbital motion like planets round the sun—a miniature solar system, in fact, in which the vacant space far exceeds that occupied by matter. The nucleus, although excessively minute, its diameter being only a small fraction of a millionth of the millionth of an inch, is by no means a simple structure. It consists of a number of particles charged with positive electricity, called protons, and a number of other particles charged with negative electricity, which carry the same charge as, and may be identical with, the electrons which revolve outside the nucleus.

Under the action of great heat the outermost of the atomic electrons begin to break loose from the atom and fly off at a tangent, just as, when water is heated up, the outer molecules break loose and set off on independent journeys of their own. Finally the water is wholly evaporated; the heat has transformed it into a mass of gas (steam) in which each separate molecule flies along its own individual path, like the bullets on a battlefield. In precisely the same way, the application of heat to the atoms causes successive layers of electrons to break loose from their moorings, and the atoms become smaller and smaller until finally no coherent structure remains but merely a powdered *débris* of atomic constituents, each nucleus and electron going its own way regardless of the rest.

We cannot study the process to any extent in the laboratory since we cannot command high enough temperatures. It is just beginning in hot flames and in the electric arc. The atmospheres of stars are at higher temperatures than any obtainable on earth, and here the process is further advanced; the spectroscope shews that the atoms may be broken into two, three or even four pieces. The temperatures in the interiors of the stars are higher still, and although we cannot measure them directly we can calculate them with very fair precision. The temperature at the centre of the sun is found to be in the neighbourhood of 50,000,000 degrees, and this is a fairly average temperature for the stars in general. It is difficult to form any conception of the physical meaning of a temperature which is so far removed from anything in our experience. If a piece of matter the size of a pea could be maintained at this temperature it would scorch and shrivel up anyone who ventured within a thousand miles of it; its directed beam would destroy an army in an instant. Nevertheless, the mathematician need not hesitate to thrust his calculations right into the very hearts of the stars, and he can shew, with something approaching very near to certainty, that at the centres of most of the stars nearly all, or perhaps quite all, of the electrons must have broken loose from their parent atoms, leaving the stellar matter almost or quite pulverized into its constituent nuclei and electrons.

When I first put forward this view in 1917, I thought it was entirely novel, but I have since found that in 1644 Descartes had conjectured that the sun and fixed stars were made of matter "which possesses such violence of agitation that, impinging upon other bodies, it gets divided into indefinitely minute particles". My own suggestion was not conjecture, but was an inevitable deduction from modern knowledge of atomic physics. Since it was put forward, a great deal of labour has been devoted to testing the hypothesis that practically all the electrons have broken loose from their atoms, the stripped atoms and electrons flying about in a general hurly-burly like the molecules of a gas. But the hypothesis has proved disappointing, and a much more probable hypothesis is, I think, that the atoms are not stripped quite bare, but that in most stars they retain a few rings of electrons which give the atoms so much size that they jostle one another about like the molecules of a liquid. This hypothesis explains beautifully the otherwise puzzling fact that the stars tend to fall into distinct groups, of what may almost be described as 'standardised' sizes. On the 'liquid star' hypothesis, these different sizes correspond to the different sizes possible for the stellar atons, which may have 0, 1, 2, or 3 rings of electrons left, but cannot have fractional numbers. The largest stars of all, such as Betelgeux, have three rings left, while minute stars, such as Van Maanen's star, consist of atoms most of which are stripped quite bare, so that there is almost no limit to the closeness with which they can be packed together. These stars of course represent extremes of size; more normal stars such as Sirius, Procyon and the Sun consist mainly of atoms in which one ring of electrons is left revolving about the nucleus.

Thus the observed sizes of the stars proclaim the secret of the structure of the atom. The sizes of the stars are discontinuous because the sizes of atoms broken down to different stages are discontinuous. These discontinuities can be traced in turn to the discontinuities which form the central feature of the new system of quantum dynamics, which is now known to dominate the whole of atomic physics. Thus the distinguishing characteristic of the laws which govern the most minute processes in Nature is transmitted directly into the large scale phenomena of astronomy and governs the distribution of the huge masses of the stars. The infinitely great is never very far from the infinitely small in science, but it would be hard to find a more sensational illustration of the unity of science than that just given.

On this hypothesis, not only do the observed sizes of the stars disclose the general structure of the atom, which is old knowedge, but they also reveal the detailed structure of the particular atoms of which the stars are composed, and this is new knowledge. The more complex the structure of an atom is, the higher the temperature needed to break it up. We find that simple atoms would be completely broken up in the interiors of the stars; no coherent atomic structure would remain. To retain the various sizes demanded by the theory of liquid stars, the stellar atoms must be heavier and more complex than any atoms known on earth. The atoms which reveal their presence in the spectra of the stars are, of course, atoms of the ordinary terrestrial elements—hydrogen, iron, calcium, and the like. These, being the lightest atoms in the star, must naturally float up to its surface and so determine its spectrum. Moreover, as the earth was originally formed out of the surface of the sun, the earth is necessarily composed of the same light elements. But it now appears likely that down in the depths of the stars are other unknown and heavier atoms. Later on, we shall find another reason why this must be so, namely that no terrestrial atoms, not even radium or uranium, can produce anything like the amount of energy which these stellar atoms are observed to produce.

The Immensity of Time

The immensity of space is paralleled by that of time. We can estimate the ages of stars from the impression that time has made upon them, just as we estimate the age of a tree from the number of subdivisions of its stem, or of rings in its cross section. There are three principal methods of doing this. The orbits of binary stars, which are circular at birth, are gradually knocked out of shape by the forces from passing stars. As we can calculate the rate at which this process occurs, the shape of stars' orbits can be made to reveal their ages. The moving clusters provide a second method. Groups of bright stars such as the Great Bear, the Pleiades, Orion's Belt, are often found to consist of exceptionally massive stars which move in regular orderly formation through a jumble of slighter stars, like a flight of swans through a confused crowd of rooks and starlings. Swans, however, are conscious beings, and continually adjust their flight so as to preserve their formation. The swan-like stars cannot do this, so that their orderly formation must in time be broken by the gravitational pull of other stars. When this happens, the lighter stars are naturally knocked out of formation first, while the most massive stars retain their formation longest. This agrees with what is observed, and as we can calculate the time necessary to knock out the lighter stars, we can at once deduce the ages of those which are left in. A third method of investigation rests upon a rather abstruse dynamical theorem, which shows that after a sufficient time the energies of motion of the different types of stars must tend to equality, the little stars making up for the smallness of their mass by the rapidity of their motion. Dr. Seares, of Mount Wilson Observatory, has shown that the stars near the sun have nearly attained to this ideal state, and as we can calculate the time needed to establish it, we can again deduce the ages of the stars.

It is gratifying and significant that all three lines of investigation lead to the same result: the stars are found to be some millions of millions of years old, perhaps from five to ten millions of millions. We cannot state their ages with much precision, but it is the general order of magnitude, not the exact figure, that is important.

The Source of Stellar Radiation

Year after year, century after century, for millions of millions of years, the sun radiates enough energy from each square inch of its surface to keep a fifty horse-power engine continually in action; still hotter stars may radiate as much as 30,000 horse-power per square inch. If this energy were produced by the combustion of coal, the stars would all be completely burnt out in a few hundreds or thousands of years. Where, then, shall we find a source of energy to last millions of millions of years?

More than twenty years ago I directed attention to the enormous store of energy made available by the annihilation of matter, by positively and negatively charged protons and electrons falling into and annihilating one another, thus setting free the whole of their intrinsic energy as radiation. On this scheme neither energy nor matter had a permanent existence, but only a sort of sum of the two; each was, theoretically at least, convertible into the other.

When I put forward this hypothesis, I thought I was advocating something entirely revolutionary and unheard-of, but I have since found that Newton had anticipated something very similar exactly two centuries earlier. In his *Opticks* (1704) we find:

"*Query* 30. Are not gross bodies and
"light convertible into one another; and
"may not bodies receive much of their
"activity from the particles of light which
"enter into their composition?

"The changing of bodies into light, and
"light into bodies, is very conformable
"to the course of Nature, which seems
"delighted with transmutations. Water,
"which is a very fluid, tasteless salt, she
"changes by heat into vapour, which is
"a sort of air; and by cold into ice, which
"is hard, pellucid, brittle, fusible stone;
"and this stone returns into water by heat,
"and vapour returns into water by cold. . .
"Eggs grow from insensible magnitudes,
"and change into animals; tadpoles, into
"frogs; and worms, into flies. All birds,
"beasts and fishes, insects, trees, and
"other vegetables, with their several parts,
"grow out of water and watery tinctures

"and salts; and by putrefaction, return
"again into watery substances. And water,
"standing a few days in the open air,
"yields a tincture, which (like that of
"malt) by standing longer yields a sediment
"and a spirit; but before putrefaction is fit
"nourishment for animals and vegetables.
"And among such various and strange
"transmutations, why may not Nature
"change bodies into light, and light
"into bodies?"

For reasons which will appear later, it is highly improbable that light is ever transformed into matter, but the falling together of positively charged atomic nuclei and negatively charged electrons provides an obvious mechanism for the transformation of matter into energy, and, as we shall now see, it is practically certain that this is the actual source of the radiation of the stars.

A beam of radiation exerts pressure on any surface it falls upon, just as a jet of water does or a blast of air. The reason is that radiation carries mass about with it, and electromagnetic theory tells us the amount of this mass. For example, we can calculate that a searchlight which is radiating 50 horse-power of energy is discharging mass into space with the radiation at the rate of a gramme and a quarter a century; with sufficiently delicate adjustments it might even be possible to observe the recoil of the searchlight. Indeed, the pressure of radiation has actually been measured, although not in this particular way. New mass is of course being continually fed into the searchlight by the electric current; if it were not so, the searchlight would weigh a gramme and a quarter less after functioning for a century, this being the weight of the light it had emitted in this period of time.

Each square inch of the sun's surface is in effect a searchlight discharging radiation into space at the rate of 50 horse-power, and so is discharging mass at the rate of a gramme and a quarter a century, and the sun's surface is so large that the sun as a whole is discharging mass into space at the rate of 250 million tons a minute. Now the sun has no source of replenishment. It must have weighed 360,000 million tons more yesterday than to-day, and by to-morrow will weigh 360,000 million tons less. These are not mere speculative statements; they rest on observation, and on generally accepted principles which are directly confirmed by observation.

Allowing for the fact that a more massive star emits more radiation than a less massive one, we can calculate that five or ten million million years ago the sun must have been several times as massive as it is to-day, so that it has already lost most of the mass it had at birth. Of each ton it had at birth only a few hundredweights at most remain to-day. The loss of mass which accompanies radiation is, then, no mere academic hair-splitting. It is a real astronomical phenomenon, and young stars must be many times as massive as old stars.

There is a certain amount of direct evidence of this change of mass. The radiation of the stars imposes an endlessly recurring capital levy upon their masses, which, as observation shows, is graduated and increases very steeply indeed for the richest stars. The levy makes all the stars poorer, but it also tends to equalise what wealth remains; the older the stars get, the more nearly equal their impoverished masses become. This is a large part of the reason why the stars are nearly equal in mass. The process is most clearly marked in the binary systems, which have been formed by a single star breaking into two. The two component stars of such a system are necessarily of the same age, and it is a matter of observation that the small stars of old systems are nearer to equality of mass than the massive stars of young systems.

Thus observation and theory agree in indicating that the universe is melting away into radiation. Our position is that of polar bears on an iceberg that has broken loose from the icepack surrounding the pole, and is inexorably melting away as the iceberg drifts to warmer latitudes and ultimate extinction.

The Annihilation of Matter

Five million million years ago the sun had stored up within itself the energy which was destined to provide its light and heat until to-day, and the mass of this energy was many times the present mass of the sun. No means is known by which so much mass could be stored except in the form of electrons and protons. Thus we must suppose that the radiation of the sun through these millions of millions of years has been produced by the annihilation of electrons and protons which existed in it originally, but no longer exist now. These electrons and protons are pure bottled energy; the continuous breakage of these bottles in the sun sets free the radiation which warms and lights our earth, and enough unbroken bottles remain to provide light and heat for millions of millions of years to come.

The amount of energy made available in this way is amazing. The annihilation of a pound of coal a week would produce as much energy as the combustion of the five million tons a week which are mined in the British Isles; an ounce of coal a month would provide locomotive power for all the British railways, while a single drop of oil would take the *Mauretania* across the Atlantic. When we speak of the efficiency of a steam engine as 5 per cent. or so, we regard complete use of the thermal energy of combustion as 100 per cent. efficiency. If we measure the work done against the total intrinsic energy of the fuel, as made available by its complete annihilation, the efficiency is more like 0·00000001 per cent. On this scale the efficiency of the sun and stars is exactly 100·00 per cent.

Modern physical theory shows that the annihilation of an electron must produce a single flash of radiation of wave-length far shorter than any we can produce on earth. As this radiation threads its way through a star, its wave-length is continually increased, or, to use the technical term, the radiation is continually softened. In time it becomes γ-radiation, then hard X-radiation, then soft X-radiation, and finally it emerges from the surface of the star as ordinary light and heat. Consider, however, an electron which is annihilated not inside a star but outside in free space, or in one of the almost transparent nebulæ. The short wave-length radiation now undergoes no softening, but travels on until it meets something capable of checking it Thus all astronomical bodies, including the surface of the earth, ought to be under continual bombardment by radiation of shorter wave-length, and consequently of greater penetrating powers, than any we can produce on earth.

Highly Penetrating Radiation

Many years ago such radiation was detected in the earth's atmosphere by Prof. McLennan, now of Toronto, by Sir Ernest Rutherford, and other observers; it has recently been studied in detail by Prof. Millikan of Pasadena and others. There is no reason to doubt that it originates just where it ought to, namely in the great nebulæ, and its amount is about what it ought to be, if it is evidence of the whole universe melting away into radiation. The wave-length of the radiation might be expected to reveal the physical process by which it is generated, but the evidence is a bit puzzling. The hardest terrestrial radiation penetrates inches of lead and corresponds to a voltage of hundreds of thousands of volts. The cosmic radiation penetrates about five yards of lead, and the hardest rays are now found to correspond to about 60 million volts. Prof. Millikan was at one time inclined to attribute the rays to the combination of four atoms of hydrogen to form an atom of helium, but rays so produced would only be of the hardness corresponding to 30 million volts. There are many ways known to physics of softening radiation, but none of hardening it. Thus we must look for some source more energetic than the synthesis of hydrogen into helium, and I can see no possible stopping-place short of the annihilation of matter. Again, we are not dealing with a minute phenomenon of mere academic interest. In a sense this radiation is the most fundamental physical phenomenon of the whole universe, most regions of space containing more of it than of visible light or heat. Our bodies are traversed by it night and day. Short of going down into a mine or in a submarine we cannot escape it, and it is so intense that it breaks up several million atoms in each of our bodies every second. It may be essential to life or it may be killing us.

The Final End of Radiation

There has been much discussion as to the ultimate fate of astronomical radiation. An almost infinitesimal fraction strikes the earth in the various forms of sunlight, starlight and highly-penetrating radiation, and further minute fractions must similarly strike, and be absorbed by, other bodies in space, but the vast majority will merely wander on and on without ever meeting a target of any kind. So long as space was believed to be infinite in extent, radiation could be imagined to travel for ever onwards, but in a finite universe it can only travel round and round like a squirrel in a cage. It has been suggested that the radiation poured out from millions of millions of stars through millions of millions of years may ultimately cause space to become overcrowded with radiation, just as a cage would become overcrowded with squirrels if we kept putting them in and never took any out. Or again, it may be as though we kept putting lump after lump of sugar into the same cup of tea until finally the tea became saturated with sugar and refused to dissolve any more, at any rate unless some of the sugar already in solution crystallised out afresh as new sugar.

Calculation shews that the universe is in no danger of approaching either of these conditions. Let us pass at once to the extreme limit and imagine every atom of the present universe, stars, nebulæ and all else, suddenly transformed into radiation. We can estimate how much matter there is in the average cubic mile of the present universe, and so can calculate how much radiation there would be to the cubic mile if this matter all dissolved into radiation. We find that it would only raise the temperature of space from absolute zero to about eleven degrees above absolute zero, or to — 262 degrees Centigrade, a temperature well below that of liquid air. It is known that the temperature of the earth's surface is determined almost entirely by the amounts of heat and light it receives from the sun, the radiation from all other stars, including that wandering round and round space, contributing practically nothing. We can calculate that if the whole universe, apart from the sun, were suddenly to melt into radiation, the temperature of the earth would be raised less than a five-thousandth part of a degree, and, except for the stars being blotted out, we should notice absolutely nothing. The radiation of ten thousand dead universes may even now, for ought we know, be wandering round space; nothing less than the radiation from hundreds of thousands would be susceptible of scientific measurement. Thus we cannot tell how many universes may have perished into radiation and be wandering in this ghostly form around space, but there is certainly ample room for one more.

With an ardour equalled only by that of man's longing for personal immortality, many seem to desire that the universe itself should prove in some way to be immortal. Science sees matter being annihilated here, they argue, and its energy transformed into radiation, but in other parts of the universe this very radiation may be forming new heavens and a new earth; the tide only ebbs on our shores because it is rising on some other distant shore unknown to us.

The considerations we have just mentioned are sufficient to dispose of any such belief, but the matter can be further tested by direct numerical calculation. We have seen that if space starts empty of all radiation the melting away of our present universe will raise its temperature by about 11 degress. And calculation shews that the universe will not become saturated with radiation, in the way in which the tea may become saturated with sugar, until it reaches a temperature of 7,500,000,000,000 degrees. At this temperature, and not before, space refuses to absorb any more radiation, or if it does, it rids itself of an equivalent amount by forming new matter out of it. And to raise space to this temperature would require the dissolution of some 3×10^{47} universes similar to our present universe. The number is millions of times greater than the number of grains of sugar that could be melted in the Atlantic before this began to crystallise out into new sugar. Thus the melting away of the whole of the present universe into radiation is something less than the melting of a single grain of sugar in the Atlantic, and the radiation of the stars is as far from creating new worlds as is the sweetness of a single grain of sugar from turning an ocean into candy. Space is so vast by comparison with the amount of matter it contains that our simile of melting lumps of sugar in a tea-cup was wrongly conceived; we ought rather to have discussed the dropping of a single grain of sugar into the Atlantic.

We may sum up by saying that the

capacity of space for radiation is practically infinite when judged by any amount of radiation which can ever be poured into it. It follows that the transformation of matter into radiation is a "one-way", or as it is technically called, an "irreversible" process. Matter can change into radiation, but under present conditions radiation can never change back into matter. Ultimately a time must come when every atom which is capable of dissolving into radiation will have done so. The universe is like a clock which is running down, a clock which, so far as science knows, no one ever winds up, which cannot wind itself up, and so must stop in time. It is at present a partially wound-up clock, which must, at some time in the past have been wound up in some manner unknown to us. By studying the mechanism of the clock, and noting the length of spring which is still coiled up and the length already uncoiled, we can estimate the length of time the clock has still to run, and the length of time since it was wound up, but we can obtain no evidence as to the way in which it was originally wound up and set going.

Our scientific ancestors of half a century ago were wont to regard the universe as a fortuitous concourse of atoms which, created they knew not when or how, had fallen together and chanced to form the earth and the starry heavens. The wider knowledge of to-day shews that the main mass and the main energy of the universe do not exist in the form of atoms but of intangible radiation. We may say that the universe is mainly a universe of radiation, combined, in a far lesser degree, with the atoms out of which radiation is continually being formed. Can we regard this new universe as a fortuitous concourse of atoms and radiation ?

The analogy of the clock at once suggests a negative answer, which exact calculation emphatically confirms. A fortuitous concourse of any ingredients whatever must after sufficient time reach a state which the physicist describes as a "condition of maximum entropy", but which for the sake of brevity we may call the "final state"; it is the state of the clock which has run completely down. No matter how the ingredients start, provided they are always the same ingredients, their final state is always the same. If the ingredients are a cup of tea and four lumps of sugar, the final state is a uniform mass of sticky liquid of rather sickly sweetness, and this is always just the same, no matter how or where or in what order I put the four lumps of sugar in my tea.

The final state of the universe admits of very exact calculation. We only need to know the ingredients, which are matter and radiation; we do not need to know either their present arrangement or distribution, or the mechanism by which the universe works towards its final state. All roads lead to Rome and Rome is very easily located. Calculation shows that in the final state the odds against even a single atom which is capable of dissolving into radiation remaining undissolved are quite unthinkably great, being something like $10^{420,000,000,000}$ to one. Since many such atoms are still undissolved, we may dismiss the possibility of the present universe being in its final state. Now the odds against the present division of the total energy of the universe into atoms and radiation being fortuitous are, as it happens, precisely the same as the odds against the universe having reached its final state; indeed the mathematical specification of a fortuitous state is precisely the same as that of a final state, and this enables us to dismiss the fortuitous conception of the universe as being entirely out of the question. Everything points with overwhelming force to a definite event, or series of events, of creation at some time or times, not infinitely remote. The universe cannot have originated by chance out of its present ingredients, and neither can it have been always the same as now. For in either of these events no atoms would be left save such as are incapable of dissolving into radiation; there would be neither sunlight nor starlight but only a cool glow of radiation uniformly diffused through space. This is, indeed, so far as present-day science can see, the final end towards which all creation moves, and at which it must, at long last, arrive.

> "Then star nor sun shall waken,
> Nor any change of light;
> Nor sound of waters shaken,
> Nor any sound or sight: . . .
> Only the sleep eternal
> In an eternal night."

The Evolution of Stellar Matter

Let us now turn our attention from stellar radiation to the stellar atoms which produce this radiation by self-annihilation. The fundamental process by which radiation is released is the falling into one another of a pair of oppositely charged electric particles. When this happens the particles annihilate one another and disappear. In their place appears a splash of radiant energy which travels through the star until, after innumerable absorptions and re-emissions, it reaches the star's surface and wanders off into space. Each splash is similar to the splashes produced by radio-active material in the spinthariscope, except for being many thousands of times more powerful. The great energy of the splashes is to some extent counterbalanced by their rarity. In the sun, for example, only about one atom in every 10^{17} annihilates itself each hour. A cubic inch of the sun's mass contains, let us say, 10^{23} atoms, and of these about 1,000,000 are annihilated every hour. The energy produced in a cubic inch of the sun's mass is thus not very great, averaging about 150,000 ergs per hour, which is roughly the energy of a hundred-thousandth part of a candle-power; the enormous flow of energy from the sun's surface results from the fact that all the energy produced in a cone 433,000 miles in depth has to stream out through the mouth of this cone.

We naturally inquire what types of atoms can be responsible for the generation of this radiation. The sun's present radiation is such as would be produced by an average generation of two ergs per second for each gramme of its mass, and to the best of our knowledge it has generated and radiated at this, or a greater, rate, for some millions of millions of years. Could the sun have any such radiating capacity if its interior were formed of the common terrestrial elements, hydrogen, oxygen, calcium, iron, silicon, etc.?

One's first impulse is to say, No. Even if the sun were built of pure uranium, its radiating power would be only about one-half of that observed, and would only last for a minute fraction of what is believed to have been the sun's life. A sun of pure radium would radiate more than enough for the moment, but its life would be limited to a few thousand years. No possible combination of terrestrial elements can give the combination of high radiation and of staying power which is observed in the sun and stars.

We must, however, remember that stellar interiors are at pressures and temperatures which are quite unattainable in our laboratories. We are led to wonder whether our terrestrial elements would behave quite differently if they were exposed to stellar conditions. Is it possible, for example, that the sun's interior is formed of ordinary terrestrial elements, which owe their high generation of energy merely to their high temperatures and pressures ? Or, to put the question in a more general form, does the generation of energy proceed more merrily, do the electrons and protons annihilate one another more frequently, when the stellar matter is in a state of high temperature and pressure ? Are atomic suicides more frequent when the heat and pressure are greater ?

General theoretical physics frowns on any such suggestion, while dynamical theory demurs to it on the grounds that it would probably cause the whole universe to turn explosively into radiation. But perhaps the most direct argument against the suggestion is provided by observational astronomy.

The stars which are observed to radiate most energetically are not, broadly speaking, those in which the stellar material is at the highest temperatures and pressures. Indeed such stars are often enough put to shame in the matter of radiation by cool stars in which the pressure is low. The star S. Doradus, which we have mentioned as being the most luminous of known stars, is also one of the coolest and its interior is at an exceptionally low pressure, while Wolf 359, the least luminous of known stars, has stupendous temperatures and pressures in its interior. If we arrange the stars in order of their energy of radiation per unit mass, we shall find we have arranged them neither in order of temperature nor of pressure, but in order of their weights; the most massive stars radiate most energetically. And, as the life history of a star consists primarily of a continuous loss of weight as its substance melts away into radiation, the heaviest stars are also the youngest and the least massive stars are the oldest. We accordingly find that the stars which radiate most energetically in proportion to their masses are the youngest stars, regardless of their interior temperatures and pressures; the older stars appear to be tired out.

Now if the radiation of the stars emanated from ordinary terrestrial matter raised to high temperatures and pressures we should expect to find those stars in which the temperatures and pressures were highest radiating the most energetically. This is emphatically not observed. Instead we find that energetic radiation is an accompaniment of stellar youth. We conclude that radiation proceeds from types of matter which annihilate themselves, and so disappear altogether, as the star ages. We cannot say for certain that our terrestrial atoms contribute nothing at all, but they can at best contribute very little. If the average atom of the earth generated even a ten-thousandth part as much energy as the average atom of the sun, the earth's surface would be too hot for human habitation. Our terrestrial atoms have so little capacity for annihilating themselves and forming radiation that they may properly be described as "permanent". The atoms of radioactive elements of course form an exception; they probably represent the last surviving vestiges of more vigorous primeval matter, thus forming a bridge between the inert permanent atoms and the more short-lived atoms which generate the radiation of the stars.

Lucid Matter

As far back as 1692 Newton, writing to Dr. Bentley, postulated that the stars must be formed of a special "lucid" type of matter, different from ordinary terrestrial or "non-lucid" matter. As we have seen, a study of modern astronomy shews that the distinction was a sound one. It is still essential to an understanding of the main mechanism of the universe. The distinction is not quite so clear-cut as Newton thought, since the radioactive atoms probably provide a sort of bridge or transition between the two. The lucid atoms are probably the "parents" of the radioactive atoms, just as the latter are, at least in part, the "parents" of the permanent atoms. The scheme to which we are led may be indicated diagrammatically as follows :—

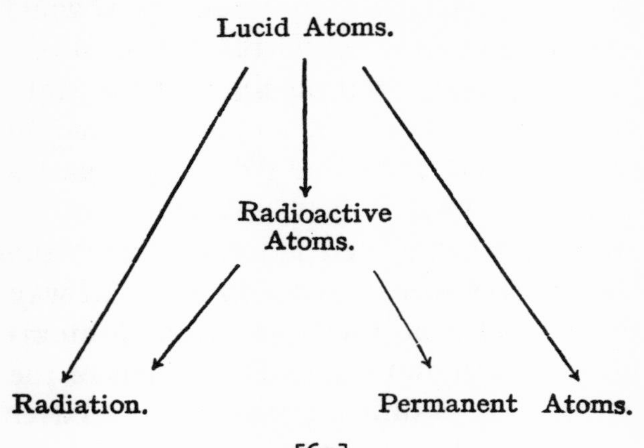

There are probably 92 types of atoms existing on earth, although two of these have not yet been identified or isolated. They are distinguished by the number of electrons which revolve about the central nucleus, this number being commonly called the "atomic number". It ranges from 1 in hydrogen, which is the lightest and simplest atom possible, up to 92 in uranium, the heaviest and most complex of all atoms known on earth. It is significant that all the atoms with atomic numbers below 84 are 'permanent', shewing no tendency to change into simpler elements or radiation, while all with atomic numbers above 83 are 'radioactive', continually changing into simpler atoms and into radiation, and so disappearing from the earth even as we write and read.

As we have been led to look on the radioactive elements as being a half-way house between the 'permanent' atoms of the earth and the 'lucid' atoms of the stars, it is natural to expect these latter to have atomic numbers higher than 92; indeed there is hardly any alternative open to us, since all but two of the first 92 places are already known to be occupied by terrestrial atoms. This fits in exactly with the requirements of the theory of liquid stars, which, as we have already seen, requires stellar atoms to be just a bit heavier and more complex than uranium, so as to resist being completely broken up by the intense heat of stellar interiors.

The lucid atoms being the heaviest atoms in a star, must naturally sink to its centre, while the permanent atoms, being the lightest, float to the surface. Thus the atoms which reveal their presence in the spectre of the sun and stars, in the light emitted by their outermost surfaces, can be only the lightest of the atoms existing in the star. The earth, formed originally out of the sun's outer layers, can only contain the lightest of the atoms existing in the sun. This is why the earth contains only permanent atoms which do not dissolve into radiation. This circumstance alone makes life possible on earth, for if the earth contained any appreciable proportion of lucid atoms it would be too hot for us to live on. The same circumstance endows the earth with a kind of melancholy immortality; it is exempt from the general destiny of matter to turn into radiation, and will continue to exist long after the stars have turned into darkness and all life and light have vanished from its surface.

We have to suppose that primeval matter consists of a mixture of atoms of varying atomic weights and numbers, and so of varying degrees of complexity. The lucid elements, which are the most complex, are the first to disappear, their disappearance reducing both the star's capacity for radiation and also the average complexity of its atoms. Just as, on the coast, the hardest rocks survive for longest the disintegrating action of the sea, so, in a star, the lightest element survive for longest the disintegrating action of time. Ultimately the star loses all radiating power and consists only of the lightest atoms of all, the permanent atoms.

Thus the general trend of chemical evolution in the universe as a whole appears to be from complex to simple, radiation being regarded as the simplest entity of all. This is contrary to the views of the early spectroscopists, who believed they had found evidence of a progressive change from simple to complex. They found, for example, that the spectrum of Sirius exhibited hydrogen lines very strongly and calcium lines very weakly ; in the solar spectrum the relative strength of these two sets of lines was reversed, calcium being strong and hydrogen weak. They concluded that hydrogen was specially prominent in the constitution of Sirius and calcium in that of the sun. Believing that Sirius must one day develop into a star similar to our sun, they conjectured that its substance must gradually change from hydrogen into calcium and other more complex elements, thus finding support for the long-established hypothesis that the more complex elements were formed by gradual evolution out of the simplest.

The true interpretation of these early observations, as the recent investigations of Saha, R. H. Fowler and Milne have abundantly proved, is merely that the surface of Sirius is at a temperature at which hydrogen is specially active in emitting and absorbing radiation, while the sun's surface is at a lower temperature at which hydrogen is comparatively inert, calcium, iron, etc., having become active in its place. Just as the laboratory physicist can produce different spectra from the same vacuum-tube by varying the mode and conditions of excitation, so Nature produces different spectra from the same stellar material by varying its temperature.

Clearly this circumstance robs stellar spectra of all direct evolutionary significance. The spectra of the stars merely tell us their present surface temperatures, so that, even if we could arrange the stars in order of age, a comparison of their spectra would only show whether their surfaces were becoming hotter or cooler; it would give no information as to evolutionary chemical changes occurring in their substance.

To investigate such changes we must probe down below the surface layers from which the star's spectrum emanates, and a study of the fundamental changes in the main body of the star suggests, as we have seen, an evolution from complex to simple—from the complex lucid atoms to simpler atoms and radiation. Such chemical evolution as we are acquainted with on earth, that of the radioactive elements, is in the same direction. This is the opposite direction to biological evolution, which proceeds from simple to complex. If the inanimate universe moves in the direction we suppose, biological evolution moves like a sailor who runs up the rigging in a sinking ship.

Although the range in the masses of the stars is not very great, it is far greater than can be attributed to variation in the atomic weights of the atoms of which they are composed. A very massive star such as Betelgeux, which has perhaps fifty times the weight of the sun, must contain more atoms than the sun. And, as we suppose that Betelgeux will in time shrink into a star similar to the sun, it follows that this shrinkage must be accompanied by an actual annihilation of atoms. There will be fewer atoms in Betelgeux in the future than now. It is not enough to think of the complex atoms breaking down into simpler atoms as the radioactive atoms do; they are destined to disappear completely.

Yet any 'permanent' atoms there may now be in Betelgeux must necessarily survive in the final shrunken star of perhaps only one per cent. of the mass of the present star, so that ninety-nine per cent. of the present mass must consist of non-permanent atoms. The primeval matter of the universe must then consist mainly of non-permanent atoms ; atoms of our terrestrial type are the exception rather than the rule. They are a mere by-product of the main processes of the universe, a residue of ash which persists merely because it is incapable of combustion. We begin to realise that our terrestrial physics and chemistry are only the outermost fringes of far-reaching sciences. Beyond the seashore we have explored in our laboratories lies the ocean whose existence we are just beginning to suspect.

The need for caution in our interpretation of the universe is borne in upon us with overwhelming force when we reflect that the new world in which astronomy moves to-day is all a discovery of the present century. It is not merely that our present concepts of the extent of the universe in space and of its duration in time are new revelations to us ; our understanding of its fundamental mechanism is equally new. The conversion of matter into radiation, which appears to be the primary physical process of the universe, did not come within our terrestrial purview at all until 1904. The primary matter of the universe appears to consist of elements whose existence we are only just beginning to suspect, and to exist in the state of almost completely broken-up atoms, a state of matter which, again, was not contemplated before 1917. The primary radiation of the universe is not visible light, but short-wave radiation of a hardness which would have seemed incredible at the beginning of the present century. Indeed, our whole knowledge of the really fundamental physical conditions of the universe in which we live is a growth of the last quarter of a century.

The simple explanation of this situation is to be found in the fact that life, naturally enough, begins its exploration of Nature by studying the conditions which immediately surround it; the study of the general conditions of the universe as a whole is a far more difficult task which life on this planet is only now approaching. Now the physical conditions under which life is possible form only a tiny fraction of the range of physical conditions which prevail in the universe as a whole. The very concept of life implies duration in time; there can be no life where the atoms change their make-up millions of times a second and no pair of atoms can ever become joined together. It also implies a certain mobility in space, and these two implications restrict life to the small range of physical conditions in which the liquid state is possible. Our survey of the universe has shown how small this range is in comparison with the range of the whole universe. Primeval matter must go on transforming itself into radiation for millions of millions of years to produce an infinitesimal amount of the inert ash on which life can exist. Even then, this residue of ash must not be too hot or too cold, or life will be impossible, and endless other conditions, of which we know nothing, must in all probability be satisfied before life comes into being. We cannot be too suspicious of the interpretation which our minds, trammelled with long brooding over, and experience limited to, one tiny corner, puts on the greater universe we are just beginning to discover.

THE LIVES OF THE STARS

The stars are almost certainly born in nebulæ of the type of the great extra-galactic nebulæ, such as are shown in Plates I, II, III, and IV. These nebulæ show a great variety of shapes, but a single thread connects them all; they are the shapes of huge masses of gas endowed with different amounts of rotation. So definitely is this the case that when Dr. Hubble recently tried to classify the shapes of these nebulæ, deliberately and avowedly shutting his eyes to all theoretical considerations, he found that purely observational considerations compelled him to classify them in precisely

PLATE IV

[*Mt. Wilson Observatory*

Fig. 4. The spiral nebula (N.G.C.7217).

A SPIRAL NEBULA VIEWED FULL-ON.

[*face p.* ***74***

the sequence I had predicted on theoretical grounds some ten years earlier.

A huge mass of gas which was entirely devoid of rotation would of course assume a strictly spherical shape ; rotation would flatten this shape out, just as the earth is flattened by its rotation, until ultimately most of the matter was spread out in a thin disc. We see the process beginning in Fig. 1 (p.19), it is well advanced in Fig. 2, and has assumed a rather extreme form in Fig. 3 (p. 20). Fig. 4 shows a nebula which is probably physically similar to that shown in Fig. 3, but viewed from another angle. The nebula shewn in the frontispiece is again probably similar but even more advanced. Now mathematical theory shows that the thin disc-like structure could not remain a mere featureless mass of gas. Just as the cooling of a cloud of steam causes it to condense into drops of water, so the cooling of a cloud of gas causes it to condense into detached masses. We see the phenomenon in progress in any collection of nebular photographs, such as those shewn in the present book; it is a necessary theoretical consequence of the laws of gases and the law of gravitation.

Now the same theory which predicts that the phenomenon must happen, predicts the scale on which it will happen. We can calculate how much matter will go to the formation of each 'drop', and the calculated masses of the drops come out to be just about the same as the masses of the stars. Indeed these drops are stars, and the process just described is that of the birth of stars. Unmistakable stars have been observed in the outer regions of many of the spiral nebulæ, including the nebula M 81 which figures as the frontispiece. It is naturally not possible to identify every observed spot of light with a star, but some of them show precisely the same peculiar fluctuations of light as characterise a certain class of variable star, the Cepheid variables already mentioned, and these put the

PLATE V

[*Franklin-Adams Chart*

Fig. 5. Nubecula Major (The Greater Magellanic Cloud).

A STAR CLOUD—THE PROBABLE END OF A SPIRAL NEBULA.

[*face p. 77*

identity of these particular spots of light beyond all reasonable doubt.

In these nebulæ, then, we are watching the birth of stars, the transformation of an inchoate mass of gas into an "island universe" of stars. Indeed Dr. Hubble found it necessary to end up his classification of nebulæ with clouds of stars. At one end of his continuous sequence is a nebula, shaped like a mass of rotating gas, in which not a single star is visible; at the other end a star-cloud such as the Greater Magellanic Cloud shewn in Plate V. in which nothing but stars are visible. Our galactic system of stars is probably the final product of just such a transformation, the Milky Way still recording the position of the equatorial plane of the original nebula.

We can form fairly precise estimates of the time since the stars were born, from the circumstance that they were probably far more massive at birth than they now are. If the sun continued to lose mass at precisely his present rate of 360,000 million tons a day, he would last for just about 15 million million years. Similarly if he had always radiated at his present rate, he would have had double his present mass 15×10^{12} years ago, treble his present mass 30×10^{12} years ago and so on. But we know that the rate of radiation is nothing like uniform; observation shews that the more massive stars burn up their substance far more rapidly than the less massive stars, and we may assume that when the sun was many times as massive as he now is, his rate of decay was correspondingly greater than now. Allowing for this we find that the sun would have had

double its present mass		$5 \cdot 7 \times 10^{12}$	years ago
four times	,,	$7 \cdot 1 \times 10^{12}$	,, ,,
eight	,,	$7 \cdot 4 \times 10^{12}$	,, ,,
sixteen	,,	$7 \cdot 5 \times 10^{12}$	,, ,,
thirty-two	,,	$7 \cdot 6 \times 10^{12}$	,, ,,

We notice that when, if ever, it was thirty-two times as massive as now, it would scatter half of its mass away in radiation in only 100,000 million years, so prodigal are the stars of their substance in their early years when they have plenty to spend. As a consequence of their running through the early stages of the careers at such a high speed, we can estimate the age of the sun, or of any other star, with fair accuracy without knowing what mass it started with. The above table suggests that the sun's age must almost certainly be between 5 and 8 million million years, and is in all probability between 7 and 8.

The calculation involves only the present mass of the sun, and the probable ages of other stars can be calculated in a similar way from their present masses. Stars are like children in that their weights give a fairly good indication of their ages, although no doubt a good deal must be allowed for individual peculiarities. Now when we calculate the ages of a typical sample of stars, as for instance those within a certain specified distance of the sun, we do not find that all ages are equally represented, but there is a quite marked preponderance of stars of ages between 5 and 8 million million years. A large number of stars, then, appear to be of about the age of our sun, and there is a deficiency, although by no means a complete absence, of stars which are very much older, or very much younger, than our sun. Although the situation is by no means free from difficulty, it seems reasonable to suppose that a large proportion of the stars in the neighbourhood of the sun were born by the break-up of a spiral nebula some 5 to 8 million million years ago.

Other groups of stars might of course shew different ages. And we cannot say how long the stellar matter may have been in the nebular state before it formed stars. Nothing in astronomy fixes with any precision the time since

> "the great morning of the world,
> when first
> God dawned on chaos."

Indeed we cannot say whether the

matter of the universe came into being all at once, by a distinct series of creations, or continuously. The general age of the universe is, however, likely to be comparable with that of the sample of stars just discussed.

The Birth of Planets

After their birth stars do not live entirely uneventful lives. They may meet with a variety of accidents and these result in different observed astronomical formations. A star may rotate too fast for safety, just as a flywheel may ; when this happens it breaks into two, and the two stars so formed revolve endlessly about one another as a binary system. Two stars may run into one another, although this is very rare. A more common occurrence is for two stars to escape running into one another by a narrow shave. When this happens, huge tides are raised on the two stars involved, and these may take the form of long streamers of gas, which ultimately condense into 'drops' just as did the gas in the outlying regions of the spiral nebulæ. It seems reasonably certain that the planets were formed in this way. The two nebulæ shewn in Plate VI suggest the general nature of the process, although whatever is taking place here is on a stupendous scale.

The birth of the solar system, then, resulted from the close approach of two stars; if a second star had not happened to come close to our sun, there would have been no solar system. It may be thought that with a life of millions of millions of years behind it, one star or another would have been certain to come near enough at some time to tear planets out of the body of our sun. Calculation shows the reverse; even after their long lives of millions of millions of years, only about one star in 100,000 can be surrounded by planets born in this way. A quite unusual accident is necessary to produce planets, and our sun with its

PLATE VI

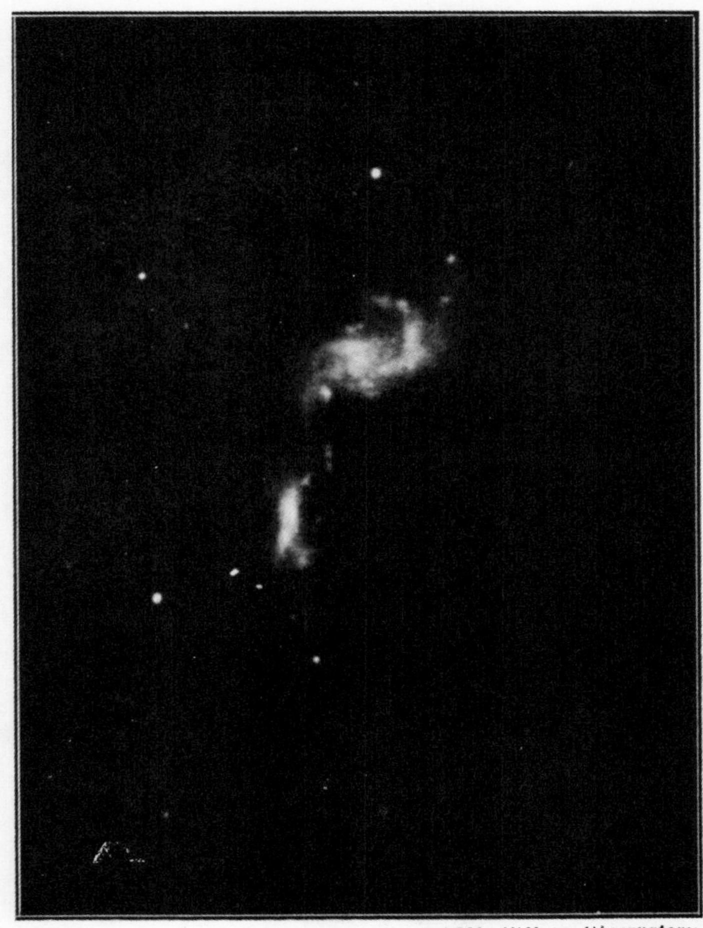

[Mt. *Wilson Observatory*

Fig. 6. Twin nebulae (4395.4401) acting tidally upon one another.

NEBULAE SUGGESTING THE WAY IN WHICH THE PLANETS MAY HAVE BEEN BORN OUT OF SUN BY THE TIDAL ACTION OF A PASSING STAR.

[*face p.* 82

family of attendant planets is rather of the nature of an astronomical freak.

In the thousand million stars surrounding our sun there are, at a moderate computation, not more than ten thousand planetary systems, because there has not been time for more than this number to be born. They are of course still coming into existence; calculation suggests a birth-rate of about one per thousand million years. Thus we should have to visit thousands of millions of stars before finding a planetary system of as recent creation as our own, and, even if life similar to our own exists on other planets, we should have to visit millions of millions of stars before finding a planet on which civilization, and interest in the outer universe, were as recent a growth as are our own. Utterly inexperienced beings, we are standing at the first flush of the dawn of civilization. Each instant the vision before us changes as the rosy-fingered goddess paints a new and ever more wonderful picture in the sky, while on earth the rolling back of the morning mists discloses new, mysterious and unsuspected vistas to our bewildered gaze. We call it living in an age of progress.

In time the glory of the morning must fade into the light of common day, and this in some far distant age will give place to evening twilight presaging the final eternal night. But we children of the dawn need give but little thought to the far-off sunset.

It may be suggested that the creation of planetary systems is also only at its beginning, and that in time every star will be surrounded, like our sun, by a family of planets. But no; the stars will have dissolved into radiation or disappeared into darkness before there is time for this to happen. So far as we can judge, our part of the universe has lived the more eventful part of its life already; what we are witnessing is less the rising of the curtain before the play than the burning out of candle-ends on an empty stage on which the drama is already over. There is not time for many more planets to be born.

Life and the Universe

The planets are the only places we know where life can exist. The stars are too hot; even their atoms are broken up by the intense heat. Nebulæ are in every way unsuitable; even if cool solid bodies exist in them, they would probably be so drenched with highly penetrating radiation as to render life impossible. We have already noticed how life demands a special type of matter, such as does not produce intense light and heat by transforming itself into radiation. We find it only in the surfaces of the stars, which are too hot for life, and in the planets which have been pulled out of these surfaces.

On any scheme of cosmogony, life must be limited to an exceedingly small corner of the universe. To our baby's wonderings whether other cradles and other babies exist, the answer appears to be that there can at best be very few cradles, and there is no conceivable means of knowing whether they are tenanted by babies or not. We look out and see a universe consisting primarily of matter which is transforming itself into radiation, and producing so much heat, light, and highly penetrating radiation as to make life impossible. In rare instances, special accidents may produce bodies such as our earth, formed of a special cool ash which no longer produces radiation, and here life may be possible. But it does not at present look as though Nature had designed the universe primarily for life; the normal star and the normal nebula have nothing to do with life except making it impossible. Life is the end of a chain of by-products; it seems to be the accident, and torrential deluges of life-destroying radiation the essential.

There is a temptation to base wide-reaching inferences on the fact that the universe as a whole is apparently antagonistic to life. Other quite different inferences might be based on the fact of our earth being singularly well-adapted to life. We shall, I think, do well to avoid both. Each oak in a forest produces many thousands of acorns, of which only one succeeds in germinating and becoming an oak. The successful acorn, contemplating myriads of acorns lying crushed, rotten, or dead on the ground, might argue that the forest must be inimical to the growth of oaks, or might reason that nothing but the intervention of a special providence could account for its own success in the face of so many failures. We must beware of both types of hasty inference.

In any case, our three-days-old infant cannot be very confident of any interpretation it puts on a universe which it only discovered a minute or two ago. We have said it has seventy years of life before it, but in truth its expectation of life would seem to be nearer to 70,000 years. It may be puzzled, distressed, and often irritated at the apparent meaninglessness and incomprehensibility of the world to which it has suddenly wakened up. But it is still very young; it might travel half the world over before finding another baby as young and inexperienced as itself. It has before it time enough and to spare in which it may understand everything. Sooner or later the pieces of the puzzle must begin to fit together, although it may reasonably be doubted whether the whole picture can ever be comprehensible to one small, and apparently quite insignificant, part of the picture. And ever the old question obtrudes itself as to whether the infant has any means of knowing that it is not dreaming all the time. The picture it sees may be merely a creation of its own mind, in which nothing really exists except itself; the universe which we study with such care may be a dream, and we brain-cells in the mind of the dreamer.